THE 12 WEEK JOURNAL

for

BOOK-BY-BOOK
Bible Study

More information at: www.123journalit.com

First Printing: January 2018
1 2 3 Journal It Publishing

ISBN-13: 978-1-947209-15-2
Forest Animals Cover Edition

TABLE OF CONTENTS:

This Journal Belongs To:

_____

How to use this JOURNAL

1) Choose 12 BOOKS  of the Bible.

2) Focus on 1 per WEEK.

3) READ all or parts of it, RESEARCH it, THINK about it, ABSORB its message, & APPLY it to your LIFE.

Brainstorm BOOK choices . . .

- use your FAVORITES
- choose by TOPIC or AUTHOR
- focus on the NEW Testament or the Old TESTAMENT
- open your Bible & start at a RANDOM spot

➡ A LITTLE TIP FOR YOU: Did you pick a long book like Psalms? No problem! Just spend a bit of extra time on it. Spread your study over a few weeks or more - or even all 12, whatever works for you!

List 12 BOOKS:

1) Proverbs

2) Songs

3) Luke

4) Matthew

5) 1 Corinthians

6) Colossians

7) Philemon

8) 2 Thessalonians

9) 1 Thessalonians

10) Joel

11) Job

12) Micha

. . . ready, set, GO ➝

Get organized for success in your Bible study!
Download your bonus free printables now:

WWW.123JOURNALIT.COM / FREEBIES

SCRIPTURE FLASHCARDS - BIBLE READING PROMPTS - JOURNALING PAGES

My BOOK choice this week:

DATE:
11-14-21

name:
Proverbs _ _ _ _ _ _ _ _ _

number of chapters: L 7 by 10 _
(TIP: divide by 6 for a per day reading plan.)

My GOALS for
this book study . . . . . .

_____
_____
_____
_____
_____
_____
_____
_____
_____

week's READING LOG

☐ date:
chapter and verses:

☐ date:
chapter and verses:

☐ date:
chapter and verses:

☐ date:
chapter and verses:

☐ date:
chapter and verses:

☐ date:
chapter and verses:

☐ date:
chapter and verses:

☐ date:
chapter and verses:

☐ date:
chapter and verses:

☐ date:
chapter and verses:

☐ date:
chapter and verses:

☐ date:
chapter and verses:

TIPS: Read all chapters or only select passages.
Split it up over 6 days with one day of rest.

Choose 3 FAVORITE verses:

1) First Pay attention to me, and then Relax.
Now you can take it easy - you're in good
hands. (Proverbs 1)

2) It's the men who walk straight who will
settle this land. The women with integrity
who will last here. (Proverbs 2)

3) _____
_____
_____

Draw & doodle one

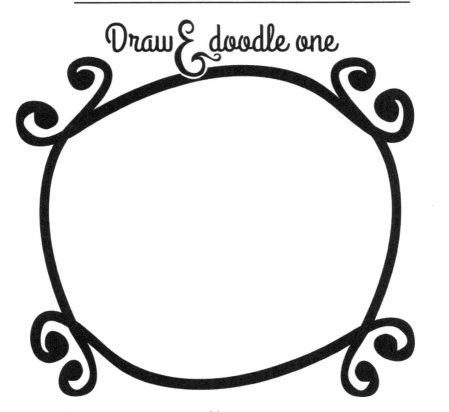

Now RESEARCH it a bit:

1. Who is the AUTHOR?

_____

2. Who was it WRITTEN to or about?

_____

_____

3. What TIME in history did it happen?

_____

_____

4. What PLACE or location is the setting?

_____

_____

5. Who are the main CHARACTERS?

_____

_____

Pick 3 CHARACTERS
& investigate more below:

1) NAME: _____

VERSE REFERENCE(S): _____

SUMMARY: _____

_____

_____

2) NAME: _____

VERSE REFERENCE(S): _____

SUMMARY: _____

_____

_____

3) NAME: _____

VERSE REFERENCE(S): _____

SUMMARY: _____

_____

_____

TIP: Characters don't have to be individual people. Use nations, tribes, animals, or even God to explore!

Study the PLACE

(HINT HINT... *search for maps online or use a Bible atlas for help.*)

DESCRIBE THE LOCATION (THINK CITIES, NATIONS, ETC.):

_____
_____
_____
_____
_____
_____

DESCRIBE THE CULTURE & PEOPLE OF THE TIME:

_____
_____
_____
_____
_____
_____
_____
_____
_____
_____
_____

Draw the MAP

(A LITTLE TIP. . . if you can't freehand draw it, trace it.)

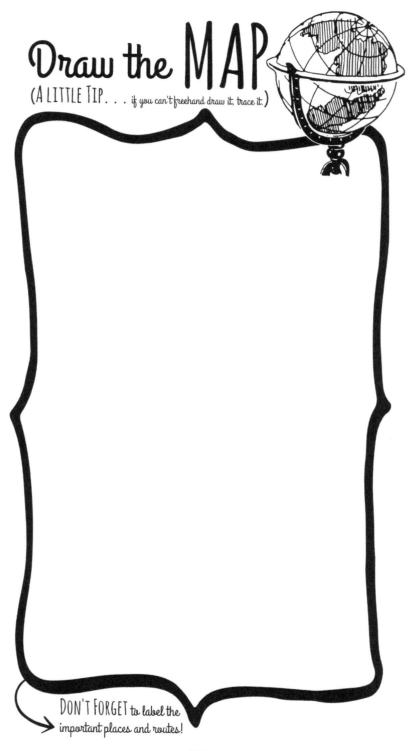

DON'T FORGET to label the important places and routes!

List the BIG THEMES

(HINT HINT. . . such as faith, mercy, love, redemption, justice, etc.)

➤ THEME(S): _____

_____

➤ VERSE REFERENCE(S): _____

_____

_____

doodle & write about it

Reflect & think about how it applies to my LIFE . . .

{

_____

_____

_____

_____

_____

_____

_____

_____

_____

_____

_____

_____

_____

_____

Go tell SOMEONE!

WHO can I tell this week?

_____

WHEN & WHERE will it happen?

_____

WHAT do I want to say?

_____

_____

WHY do I want to tell them?

_____

_____

HOW did THE PERSON receive it?

_____

_____

WHO else can I share this BOOK with?

_____

Spread the GOOD NEWS everyday . . .

extra NOTES

extra NOTES

My BOOK choice this week:

DATE:

name:

- - - - - - - - - - - - - - - - -

number of chapters: _ _ _ _
(TIP: divide by 6 for a per day reading plan.)

My GOALS for
this book study . . . . . .

_____

_____

_____

_____

_____

_____

_____

_____

_____

week's READING LOG

☐ date:
chapter and verses:

☐ date:
chapter and verses:

☐ date:
chapter and verses:

☐ date:
chapter and verses:

☐ date:
chapter and verses:

☐ date:
chapter and verses:

☐ date:
chapter and verses:

☐ date:
chapter and verses:

☐ date:
chapter and verses:

☐ date:
chapter and verses:

☐ date:
chapter and verses:

☐ date:
chapter and verses:

TIPS: Read all chapters or only select passages.
Split it up over 6 days with one day of rest.

Choose 3 FAVORITE verses:

1) _____
_____
_____

2) _____
_____
_____

3) _____
_____
_____

Draw & doodle one

Now RESEARCH it a bit:

1. Who is the AUTHOR?

_____

2. Who was it WRITTEN to or about?

_____

_____

3. What TIME in history did it happen?

_____

_____

4. What PLACE or location is the setting?

_____

_____

5. Who are the main CHARACTERS?

_____

_____

Pick 3 CHARACTERS
& investigate more below :

1) NAME: _____
   VERSE REFERENCE(S): _____
   SUMMARY: _____
   _____
   _____

2) NAME: _____
   VERSE REFERENCE(S): _____
   SUMMARY: _____
   _____
   _____

3) NAME: _____
   VERSE REFERENCE(S): _____
   SUMMARY: _____
   _____
   _____

TIP: Characters don't have to be individual people.
Use nations, tribes, animals, or even God to explore!

Study the PLACE

(HINT HINT... search for maps online or use a Bible atlas for help.)

DESCRIBE THE LOCATION (THINK CITIES, NATIONS, ETC.):

_____

_____

_____

_____

_____

_____

DESCRIBE THE CULTURE & PEOPLE OF THE TIME:

_____

_____

_____

_____

_____

_____

_____

_____

_____

_____

_____

Draw the MAP

(A LITTLE TIP. . . if you can't freehand draw it, trace it.)

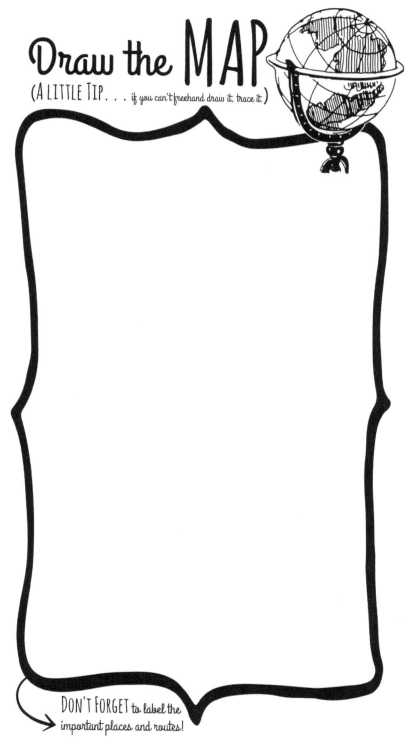

DON'T FORGET to label the important places and routes!

List the BIG THEMES

(HINT HINT. . . such as faith, mercy, love, redemption, justice, etc.)

➡ THEME(S): _____

_____

➡ VERSE REFERENCE(S): _____

_____

_____

doodle & write about it

Reflect & think about how it applies to my LIFE . . .

_____

_____

_____

_____

_____

_____

_____

_____

_____

_____

_____

_____

Go tell SOMEONE!

WHO can I tell this week?

_____

WHEN & WHERE will it happen?

_____

WHAT do I want to say?

_____

_____

WHY do I want to tell them?

_____

_____

HOW did THE PERSON receive it?

_____

_____

WHO else can I share this BOOK with?

_____

Spread the GOOD NEWS everyday . . . .

extra NOTES

extra NOTES

My BOOK choice this week:

DATE:

name:

_ _ _ _ _ _ _ _ _ _ _ _ _ _ _

number of chapters: _ _ _ _
(TIP: divide by 6 for a per day reading plan.)

My GOALS for this book study . . . . . .

_____

_____

_____

_____

_____

_____

_____

_____

_____

_____

week's READING LOG

☐ date:
chapter and verses:

☐ date:
chapter and verses:

☐ date:
chapter and verses:

☐ date:
chapter and verses:

☐ date:
chapter and verses:

☐ date:
chapter and verses:

☐ date:
chapter and verses:

☐ date:
chapter and verses:

☐ date:
chapter and verses:

☐ date:
chapter and verses:

☐ date:
chapter and verses:

☐ date:
chapter and verses:

TIPS: Read all chapters or only select passages.
Split it up over 6 days with one day of rest.

Choose 3 FAVORITE verses:

1) _____
   _____
   _____

2) _____
   _____
   _____

3) _____
   _____
   _____

Draw & doodle one

Now RESEARCH it a bit:

1. Who is the AUTHOR?

_____

2. Who was it WRITTEN to or about?

_____

_____

3. What TIME in history did it happen?

_____

_____

4. What PLACE or location is the setting?

_____

_____

5. Who are the main CHARACTERS?

_____

_____

Pick 3 CHARACTERS
& investigate more below:

1) NAME: _____
VERSE REFERENCE(S): _____
SUMMARY: _____
_____
_____

2) NAME: _____
VERSE REFERENCE(S): _____
SUMMARY: _____
_____
_____

3) NAME: _____
VERSE REFERENCE(S): _____
SUMMARY: _____
_____
_____

TIP: Characters don't have to be individual people.
Use nations, tribes, animals, or even God to explore!

Study the PLACE

DESCRIBE THE LOCATION (THINK CITIES, NATIONS, ETC.):

_____

_____

_____

_____

_____

_____

DESCRIBE THE CULTURE & PEOPLE OF THE TIME:

_____

_____

_____

_____

_____

_____

_____

_____

_____

_____

_____

_____

Draw the MAP

(A LITTLE TIP. . . if you can't freehand draw it, trace it.)

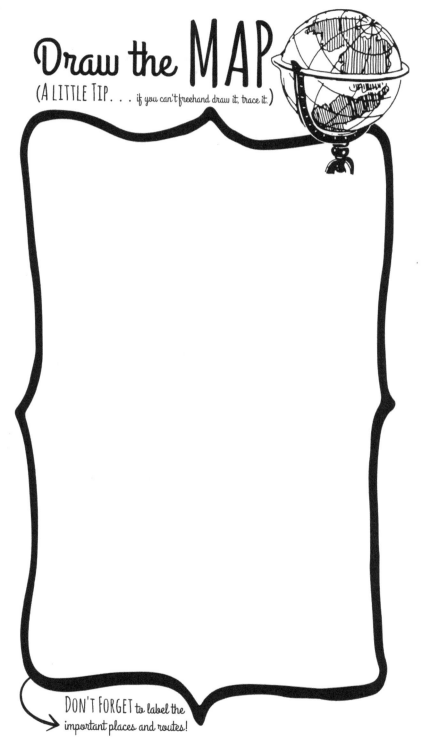

DON'T FORGET to label the important places and routes!

List the BIG THEMES

(HINT HINT. . . such as faith, mercy, love, redemption, justice, etc.)

➡️ THEME(S): _____

_____

➡️ VERSE REFERENCE(S): _____

_____

_____

doodle & write about it

Reflect & think about how it applies to my LIFE . . .

{

_____

_____

_____

_____

_____

_____

_____

_____

_____

_____

_____

_____

_____

_____

Go tell SOMEONE!

WHO can I tell this week?

_____

WHEN & WHERE will it happen?

_____

WHAT do I want to say?

_____

_____

WHY do I want to tell them?

_____

_____

HOW did THE PERSON receive it?

_____

_____

WHO else can I share this BOOK with?

_____

Spread the GOOD NEWS everyday . . .

extra NOTES

extra NOTES

My BOOK choice this week:

DATE:

name:
_ _ _ _ _ _ _ _ _ _ _ _ _

number of chapters: _ _ _ _
(TIP: divide by 6 for a per day reading plan.)

My GOALS for this book study . . . . . .

_____
_____
_____
_____
_____
_____
_____
_____
_____
_____

week's <u>READING LOG</u>

☐ date:
  chapter and verses:

☐ date:
  chapter and verses:

☐ date:
  chapter and verses:

☐ date:
  chapter and verses:

☐ date:
  chapter and verses:

☐ date:
  chapter and verses:

☐ date:
  chapter and verses:

☐ date:
  chapter and verses:

☐ date:
  chapter and verses:

☐ date:
  chapter and verses:

☐ date:
  chapter and verses:

☐ date:
  chapter and verses:

TIPS: Read all chapters or only select passages.
Split it up over 6 days with one day of rest.

Choose 3 FAVORITE verses:

1) _____
_____
_____

2) _____
_____
_____

3) _____
_____
_____

Draw & doodle one

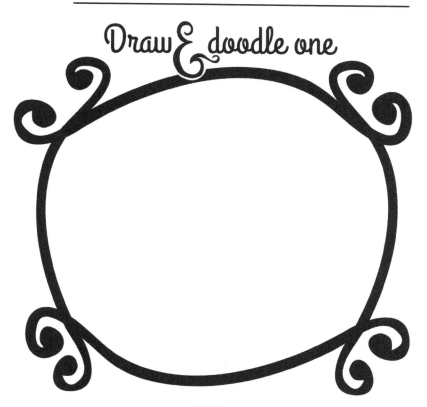

Now RESEARCH it a bit:

1. Who is the AUTHOR?

_____

2. Who was it WRITTEN to or about?

_____

_____

3. What TIME in history did it happen?

_____

_____

4. What PLACE or location is the setting?

_____

_____

5. Who are the main CHARACTERS?

_____

_____

Pick 3 CHARACTERS
& investigate more below:

1) NAME: _____
VERSE REFERENCE(S): _____
SUMMARY: _____
_____
_____

2) NAME: _____
VERSE REFERENCE(S): _____
SUMMARY: _____
_____
_____

3) NAME: _____
VERSE REFERENCE(S): _____
SUMMARY: _____
_____
_____

TIP: Characters don't have to be individual people.
Use nations, tribes, animals, or even God to explore!

Study the PLACE

(HINT HINT... *search for maps online or use a Bible atlas for help.*)

DESCRIBE THE LOCATION (THINK CITIES, NATIONS, ETC.):

_____
_____
_____
_____
_____

DESCRIBE THE CULTURE & PEOPLE OF THE TIME:

_____
_____
_____
_____
_____
_____
_____
_____
_____

Draw the MAP

(A LITTLE TIP. . . if you can't freehand draw it, trace it.)

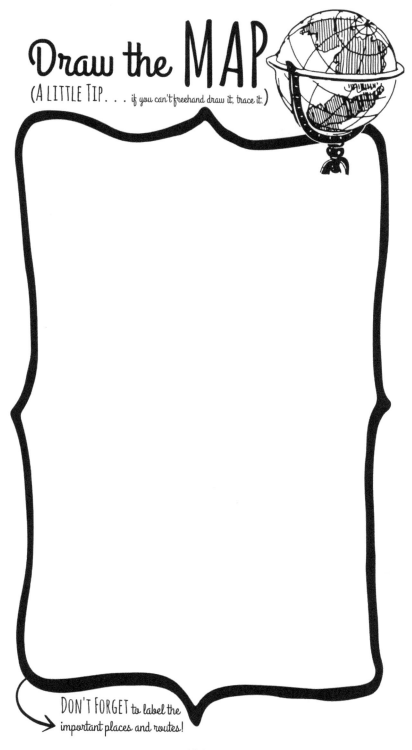

DON'T FORGET to label the important places and routes!

List the BIG THEMES

(HINT HINT. . . such as faith, mercy, love, redemption, justice, etc.)

➡️ THEME(S): _____

_____

➡️ VERSE REFERENCE(S): _____

_____

_____

doodle & write about it

Reflect & think about how it applies to my LIFE . . .

{

_____

_____

_____

_____

_____

_____

_____

_____

_____

_____

_____

_____

_____

Go tell SOMEONE!

WHO can I tell this week?

_____

WHEN & WHERE will it happen?

_____

WHAT do I want to say?

_____

_____

WHY do I want to tell them?

_____

_____

HOW did THE PERSON receive it?

_____

_____

WHO else can I share this BOOK with?

_____

Spread the GOOD NEWS everyday . . . .

extra NOTES

extra NOTES

My BOOK choice this week:

DATE:

name:

_ _ _ _ _ _ _ _ _ _ _ _ _ _ _ _

number of chapters: _ _ _ _
(TIP: divide by 6 for a per day reading plan.)

My GOALS for this book study . . . . . .

_____

_____

_____

_____

_____

_____

_____

_____

_____

_____

week's READING LOG

☐ date:
chapter and verses:

☐ date:
chapter and verses:

☐ date:
chapter and verses:

☐ date:
chapter and verses:

☐ date:
chapter and verses:

☐ date:
chapter and verses:

☐ date:
chapter and verses:

☐ date:
chapter and verses:

☐ date:
chapter and verses:

☐ date:
chapter and verses:

☐ date:
chapter and verses:

☐ date:
chapter and verses:

TIPS: Read all chapters or only select passages.
Split it up over 6 days with one day of rest.

Choose 3 FAVORITE verses:

1) _____
   _____
   _____

2) _____
   _____
   _____

3) _____
   _____
   _____

Draw & doodle one

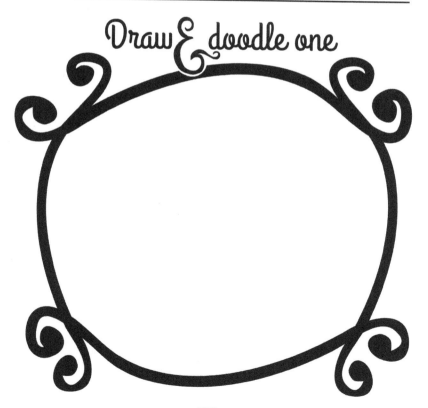

Now RESEARCH it a bit:

1. Who is the AUTHOR?

_____

2. Who was it WRITTEN to or about?

_____

_____

3. What TIME in history did it happen?

_____

_____

4. What PLACE or location is the setting?

_____

_____

5. Who are the main CHARACTERS?

_____

_____

Pick 3 CHARACTERS
& investigate more below:

1) NAME: _____

VERSE REFERENCE(S): _____

SUMMARY: _____

_____

_____

2) NAME: _____

VERSE REFERENCE(S): _____

SUMMARY: _____

_____

_____

3) NAME: _____

VERSE REFERENCE(S): _____

SUMMARY: _____

_____

_____

TIP: Characters don't have to be individual people.
Use nations, tribes, animals, or even God to explore!

Study the PLACE

(HINT HINT... *search for maps online or use a Bible atlas for help.*)

DESCRIBE THE LOCATION (THINK CITIES, NATIONS, ETC.):

_____
_____
_____
_____
_____
_____

DESCRIBE THE CULTURE & PEOPLE OF THE TIME:

_____
_____
_____
_____
_____
_____
_____
_____
_____
_____
_____

Draw the MAP

(A LITTLE TIP... if you can't freehand draw it, trace it.)

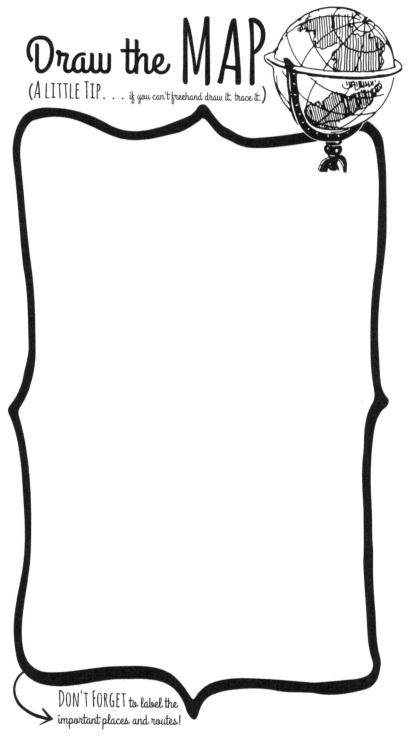

DON'T FORGET to label the important places and routes!

List the BIG THEMES

(HINT HINT. . . such as faith, mercy, love, redemption, justice, etc.)

➤ THEME(S): _____

_____

➤ VERSE REFERENCE(S): _____

_____

_____

doodle & write about it

Reflect & think about how it applies to my LIFE . . .

{

_____

_____

_____

_____

_____

_____

_____

_____

_____

_____

_____

_____

WHO can I tell this week?

_____

WHEN & WHERE will it happen?

_____
_____

WHAT do I want to say?

_____
_____
_____

WHY do I want to tell them?

_____
_____
_____

HOW did THE PERSON receive it?

_____
_____
_____

WHO else can I share this BOOK with?

_____

Spread the GOOD NEWS everyday . . .

extra NOTES

extra NOTES

My BOOK choice this week:

DATE:

name:

- - - - - - - - - - - - - - - - - - - -

number of chapters: - - - -
(TIP: divide by 6 for a per day reading plan.)

My GOALS for
this book study . . . . . .

_____

_____

_____

_____

_____

_____

_____

_____

_____

week's READING LOG

☐ date:
chapter and verses:

☐ date:
chapter and verses:

☐ date:
chapter and verses:

☐ date:
chapter and verses:

☐ date:
chapter and verses:

☐ date:
chapter and verses:

☐ date:
chapter and verses:

☐ date:
chapter and verses:

☐ date:
chapter and verses:

☐ date:
chapter and verses:

☐ date:
chapter and verses:

☐ date:
chapter and verses:

TIPS: Read all chapters or only select passages.
Split it up over 6 days with one day of rest.

Choose 3 FAVORITE verses:

1) _____
_____
_____

2) _____
_____
_____

3) _____
_____
_____

Draw & doodle one

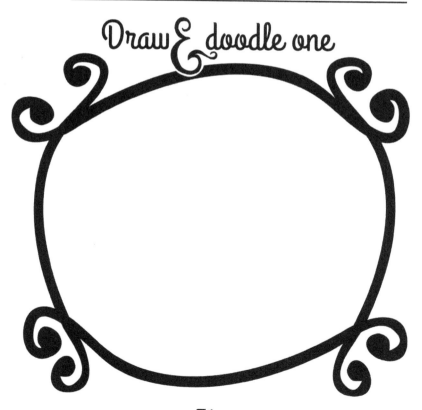

Now RESEARCH it a bit:

1. Who is the AUTHOR?

_____

2. Who was it WRITTEN to or about?

_____

_____

3. What TIME in history did it happen?

_____

_____

4. What PLACE or location is the setting?

_____

_____

5. Who are the main CHARACTERS?

_____

_____

Pick 3 CHARACTERS
& investigate more below:

1) NAME: _____

VERSE REFERENCE(S): _____

SUMMARY: _____

_____

_____

2) NAME: _____

VERSE REFERENCE(S): _____

SUMMARY: _____

_____

_____

3) NAME: _____

VERSE REFERENCE(S): _____

SUMMARY: _____

_____

_____

TIP: Characters don't have to be individual people. Use nations, tribes, animals, or even God to explore!

Study the PLACE

(HINT HINT... . *search for maps online or use a Bible atlas for help.*)

DESCRIBE THE LOCATION (THINK CITIES, NATIONS, ETC.):

_____

_____

_____

_____

_____

_____

DESCRIBE THE CULTURE & PEOPLE OF THE TIME:

_____

_____

_____

_____

_____

_____

_____

_____

_____

_____

_____

Draw the MAP

(A LITTLE TIP. . . . if you can't freehand draw it, trace it.)

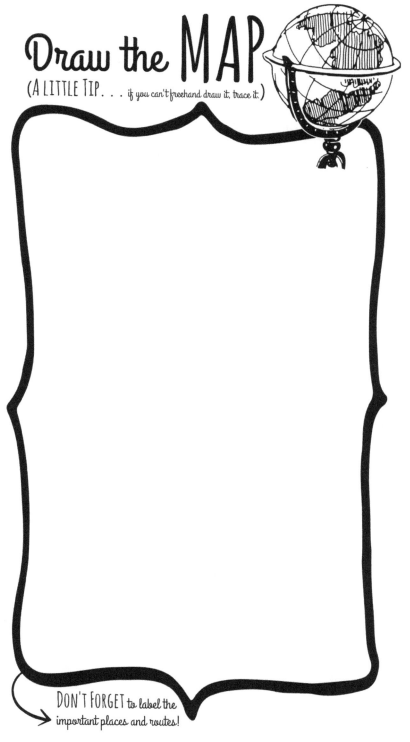

DON'T FORGET to label the important places and routes!

List the BIG THEMES

(HINT HINT. . . such as faith, mercy, love, redemption, justice, etc.)

➡ THEME(S): _____

_____

➡ VERSE REFERENCE(S): _____

_____

_____

doodle & write about it

Reflect & think about how it applies to my LIFE . . .

_____

_____

_____

_____

_____

_____

_____

_____

_____

_____

_____

_____

Go tell SOMEONE!

WHO can I tell this week?

_____

WHEN & WHERE will it happen?

_____

WHAT do I want to say?

_____

_____

WHY do I want to tell them?

_____

_____

HOW did THE PERSON receive it?

_____

_____

WHO else can I share this BOOK with?

_____

Spread the GOOD NEWS everyday . . . .

extra NOTES

extra NOTES

My BOOK choice this week:

DATE:

name:

- - - - - - - - - - - -

number of chapters: - - - -
(TIP: divide by 6 for a per day reading plan.)

My GOALS for this book study . . . . . .

_____

_____

_____

_____

_____

_____

_____

_____

_____

week's READING LOG

☐ date:
  chapter and verses:

☐ date:
  chapter and verses:

☐ date:
  chapter and verses:

☐ date:
  chapter and verses:

☐ date:
  chapter and verses:

☐ date:
  chapter and verses:

☐ date:
  chapter and verses:

☐ date:
  chapter and verses:

☐ date:
  chapter and verses:

☐ date:
  chapter and verses:

☐ date:
  chapter and verses:

☐ date:
  chapter and verses:

TIPS: Read all chapters or only select passages. Split it up over 6 days with one day of rest.

Choose 3 FAVORITE verses:

1) _____
_____
_____

2) _____
_____
_____

3) _____
_____
_____

Draw & doodle one

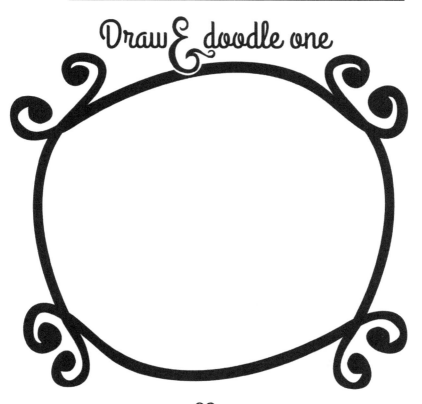

Now RESEARCH it a bit:

1. Who is the AUTHOR?

_____

2. Who was it WRITTEN to or about?

_____

_____

3. What TIME in history did it happen?

_____

_____

4. What PLACE or location is the setting?

_____

_____

5. Who are the main CHARACTERS?

_____

_____

Pick 3 CHARACTERS
& investigate more below:

1) NAME: _____
   VERSE REFERENCE(S): _____
   SUMMARY: _____
   _____
   _____

2) NAME: _____
   VERSE REFERENCE(S): _____
   SUMMARY: _____
   _____
   _____

3) NAME: _____
   VERSE REFERENCE(S): _____
   SUMMARY: _____
   _____
   _____

TIP: Characters don't have to be individual people.
Use nations, tribes, animals, or even God to explore!

Study the PLACE

(HINT HINT. . . . *search for maps online or use a Bible atlas for help.*)

DESCRIBE THE LOCATION (THINK CITIES, NATIONS, ETC.):

_____
_____
_____
_____
_____
_____
_____

DESCRIBE THE CULTURE & PEOPLE OF THE TIME:

_____
_____
_____
_____
_____
_____
_____
_____
_____
_____
_____
_____

Draw the MAP

(A LITTLE TIP... if you can't freehand draw it, trace it.)

DON'T FORGET to label the important places and routes!

List the BIG THEMES

(HINT HINT. . . such as faith, mercy, love, redemption, justice, etc.)

➡ THEME(S): _____

_____

➡ VERSE REFERENCE(S): _____

_____

_____

doodle & write about it

Reflect & think about how it applies to my LIFE . . .

_____

_____

_____

_____

_____

_____

_____

_____

_____

_____

_____

_____

Go tell SOMEONE!

WHO can I tell this week?

_____

WHEN & WHERE will it happen?

_____
_____

WHAT do I want to say?

_____
_____
_____

WHY do I want to tell them?

_____
_____
_____

HOW did THE PERSON receive it?

_____
_____
_____

WHO else can I share this BOOK with?

_____

Spread the GOOD NEWS everyday . . . .

extra NOTES

extra NOTES

My BOOK choice this week:

DATE:

name:

_ _ _ _ _ _ _ _ _ _ _ _ _ _

number of chapters: _ _ _ _
(TIP: divide by 6 for a per day reading plan.)

My GOALS for this book study . . . . . .

_____

_____

_____

_____

_____

_____

_____

_____

_____

_____

week's READING LOG

☐ date:
chapter and verses:

☐ date:
chapter and verses:

☐ date:
chapter and verses:

☐ date:
chapter and verses:

☐ date:
chapter and verses:

☐ date:
chapter and verses:

☐ date:
chapter and verses:

☐ date:
chapter and verses:

☐ date:
chapter and verses:

☐ date:
chapter and verses:

☐ date:
chapter and verses:

☐ date:
chapter and verses:

TIPS: Read all chapters or only select passages.
Split it up over 6 days with one day of rest.

Choose 3 FAVORITE verses:

1) _____
   _____
   _____

2) _____
   _____
   _____

3) _____
   _____
   _____

Draw & doodle one

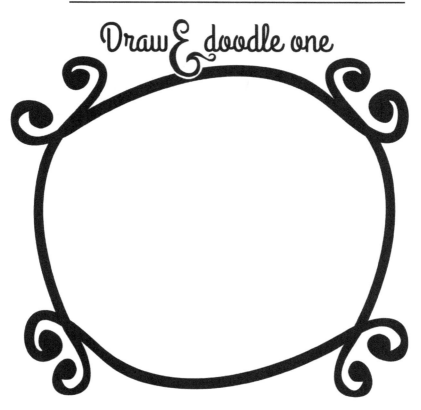

Now RESEARCH it a bit:

1. Who is the AUTHOR?

_____

2. Who was it WRITTEN to or about?

_____

_____

3. What TIME in history did it happen?

_____

_____

4. What PLACE or location is the setting?

_____

_____

5. Who are the main CHARACTERS?

_____

_____

Pick 3 CHARACTERS
& investigate more below:

1) NAME: _____

VERSE REFERENCE(S): _____

SUMMARY: _____

_____

_____

2) NAME: _____

VERSE REFERENCE(S): _____

SUMMARY: _____

_____

_____

3) NAME: _____

VERSE REFERENCE(S): _____

SUMMARY: _____

_____

_____

TIP: Characters don't have to be individual people.
Use nations, tribes, animals, or even God to explore!

Study the PLACE

(HINT HINT... *search for maps online or use a Bible atlas for help.*)

DESCRIBE THE LOCATION (THINK CITIES, NATIONS, ETC.):

_____

_____

_____

_____

_____

_____

DESCRIBE THE CULTURE & PEOPLE OF THE TIME:

_____

_____

_____

_____

_____

_____

_____

_____

_____

_____

_____

_____

Draw the MAP

(A LITTLE TIP. . . if you can't freehand draw it, trace it.)

DON'T FORGET to label the
important places and routes!

List the BIG THEMES

(HINT HINT. . . such as faith, mercy, love, redemption, justice, etc.)

 THEME(S): _____

_____

VERSE REFERENCE(S): _____

_____

_____

doodle & write about it

Reflect & think about how it applies to my LIFE . . .

{

_____

_____

_____

_____

_____

_____

_____

_____

_____

_____

_____

_____

_____

Go tell SOMEONE!

WHO can I tell this week?

_____

WHEN & WHERE will it happen?

_____

WHAT do I want to say?

_____
_____

WHY do I want to tell them?

_____
_____

HOW did THE PERSON receive it?

_____
_____

WHO else can I share this BOOK with?

_____

Spread the GOOD NEWS everyday . . .

extra NOTES

extra NOTES

My BOOK choice this week:

DATE:

name:

- - - - - - - - - - - - - - - -

number of chapters: - - - - -
(TIP: divide by 6 for a per day reading plan.)

My GOALS for
this book study . . . . . .

_____

_____

_____

_____

_____

_____

_____

_____

_____

week's READING LOG

☐ date:
chapter and verses:

☐ date:
chapter and verses:

☐ date:
chapter and verses:

☐ date:
chapter and verses:

☐ date:
chapter and verses:

☐ date:
chapter and verses:

☐ date:
chapter and verses:

☐ date:
chapter and verses:

☐ date:
chapter and verses:

☐ date:
chapter and verses:

☐ date:
chapter and verses:

☐ date:
chapter and verses:

↪ TIPS: Read all chapters or only select passages.
Split it up over 6 days with one day of rest.

Choose 3 FAVORITE verses:

1) _____
_____
_____

2) _____
_____
_____

3) _____
_____
_____

Draw & doodle one

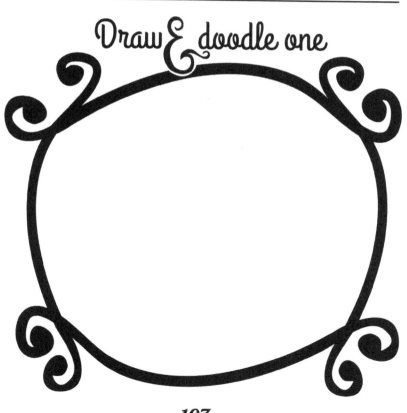

Now RESEARCH it a bit:

1. Who is the AUTHOR?

_____

2. Who was it WRITTEN to or about?

_____

_____

3. What TIME in history did it happen?

_____

_____

4. What PLACE or location is the setting?

_____

_____

5. Who are the main CHARACTERS?

_____

_____

Pick 3 CHARACTERS
& investigate more below:

1) NAME: _____

VERSE REFERENCE(S): _____

SUMMARY: _____

_____

_____

2) NAME: _____

VERSE REFERENCE(S): _____

SUMMARY: _____

_____

_____

3) NAME: _____

VERSE REFERENCE(S): _____

SUMMARY: _____

_____

_____

TIP: Characters don't have to be individual people.
Use nations, tribes, animals, or even God to explore!

Study the PLACE

(HINT HINT... *search for maps online or use a Bible atlas for help.*)

DESCRIBE THE LOCATION (THINK CITIES, NATIONS, ETC.):

_____

_____

_____

_____

_____

_____

DESCRIBE THE CULTURE & PEOPLE OF THE TIME:

_____

_____

_____

_____

_____

_____

_____

_____

_____

_____

_____

_____

Draw the MAP

(A LITTLE TIP. . . if you can't freehand draw it, trace it.)

DON'T FORGET to label the
important places and routes!

List the BIG THEMES

(HINT HINT. . . such as faith, mercy, love, redemption, justice, etc.)

➤ THEME(S): _____

_____

➤ VERSE REFERENCE(S): _____

_____

_____

doodle & write about it

Reflect & think about how it applies to my LIFE . . .

_____

_____

_____

_____

_____

_____

_____

_____

_____

_____

_____

Go tell SOMEONE!

WHO can I tell this week?

_____

WHEN & WHERE will it happen?

_____

WHAT do I want to say?

_____

_____

WHY do I want to tell them?

_____

_____

HOW did THE PERSON receive it?

_____

_____

WHO else can I share this BOOK with?

_____

Spread the GOOD NEWS everyday . . .

extra NOTES

extra NOTES

My BOOK choice this week:

DATE:

name:

_ _ _ _ _ _ _ _ _ _ _ _ _ _ _

number of chapters: _ _ _ _
(TIP: divide by 6 for a per day reading plan.)

My GOALS for this book study . . . . . .

_____

_____

_____

_____

_____

_____

_____

_____

_____

_____

week's READING LOG

☐ date:
chapter and verses:

☐ date:
chapter and verses:

☐ date:
chapter and verses:

☐ date:
chapter and verses:

☐ date:
chapter and verses:

☐ date:
chapter and verses:

☐ date:
chapter and verses:

☐ date:
chapter and verses:

☐ date:
chapter and verses:

☐ date:
chapter and verses:

☐ date:
chapter and verses:

☐ date:
chapter and verses:

TIPS: Read all chapters or only select passages.
Split it up over 6 days with one day of rest.

Choose 3 FAVORITE verses:

1) _____
   _____
   _____

2) _____
   _____
   _____

3) _____
   _____
   _____

Draw & doodle one

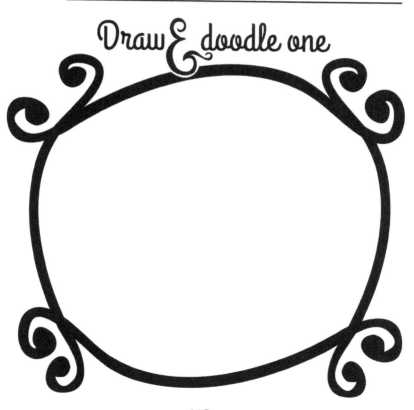

Now RESEARCH it a bit:

1. Who is the AUTHOR?

_____

2. Who was it WRITTEN to or about?

_____

_____

3. What TIME in history did it happen?

_____

_____

4. What PLACE or location is the setting?

_____

_____

5. Who are the main CHARACTERS?

_____

_____

Pick 3 CHARACTERS
& investigate more below:

1) NAME: _____
   VERSE REFERENCE(S): _____
   SUMMARY: _____
   _____
   _____

2) NAME: _____
   VERSE REFERENCE(S): _____
   SUMMARY: _____
   _____
   _____

3) NAME: _____
   VERSE REFERENCE(S): _____
   SUMMARY: _____
   _____
   _____

> TIP: Characters don't have to be individual people.
> Use nations, tribes, animals, or even God to explore!

Study the PLACE

(HINT HINT. . . . search for maps online or use a Bible atlas for help.)

DESCRIBE THE LOCATION (THINK CITIES, NATIONS, ETC.):

_____
_____
_____
_____
_____
_____

DESCRIBE THE CULTURE & PEOPLE OF THE TIME:

_____
_____
_____
_____
_____
_____
_____
_____
_____
_____
_____
_____

Draw the MAP

(A LITTLE TIP. . . . if you can't freehand draw it, trace it.)

DON'T FORGET to label the important places and routes!

List the BIG THEMES

(HINT HINT. . . such as faith, mercy, love, redemption, justice, etc.)

➡ THEME(S): _____

_____

➡ VERSE REFERENCE(S): _____

_____

_____

doodle & write about it

Reflect & think about how it applies to my LIFE . . .

{

_____

_____

_____

_____

_____

_____

_____

_____

_____

_____

_____

_____

Go tell SOMEONE!

WHO can I tell this week?

_____

WHEN & WHERE will it happen?

_____

WHAT do I want to say?

_____
_____

WHY do I want to tell them?

_____
_____

HOW did THE PERSON receive it?

_____
_____

WHO else can I share this BOOK with?

_____

Spread the GOOD NEWS everyday . . .

extra NOTES

extra NOTES

My BOOK choice this week:

DATE:

name:
- - - - - - - - - - - - - - - - - -

number of chapters: _ _ _ _
(TIP: divide by 6 for a per day reading plan.)

My GOALS for
this book study . . . . . .

_____

_____

_____

_____

_____

_____

_____

_____

_____

_____

week's READING LOG

☐ date:
chapter and verses:

☐ date:
chapter and verses:

☐ date:
chapter and verses:

☐ date:
chapter and verses:

☐ date:
chapter and verses:

☐ date:
chapter and verses:

☐ date:
chapter and verses:

☐ date:
chapter and verses:

☐ date:
chapter and verses:

☐ date:
chapter and verses:

☐ date:
chapter and verses:

☐ date:
chapter and verses:

→ TIPS: Read all chapters or only select passages.
Split it up over 6 days with one day of rest.

Choose 3 FAVORITE verses:

1) _____
   _____
   _____

2) _____
   _____
   _____

3) _____
   _____
   _____

Draw & doodle one

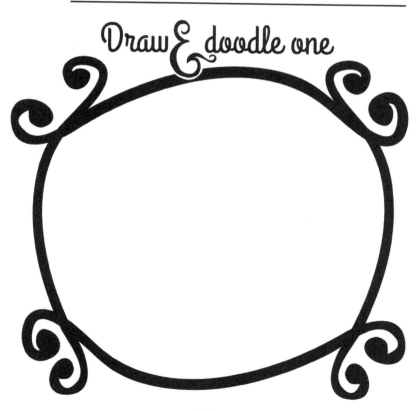

Now RESEARCH it a bit:

1. Who is the AUTHOR?

_____

2. Who was it WRITTEN to or about?

_____

_____

3. What TIME in history did it happen?

_____

_____

4. What PLACE or location is the setting?

_____

_____

5. Who are the main CHARACTERS?

_____

_____

Pick 3 CHARACTERS
& investigate more below:

1) NAME: _____

VERSE REFERENCE(S): _____

SUMMARY: _____

_____

_____

2) NAME: _____

VERSE REFERENCE(S): _____

SUMMARY: _____

_____

_____

3) NAME: _____

VERSE REFERENCE(S): _____

SUMMARY: _____

_____

_____

TIP: Characters don't have to be individual people.
Use nations, tribes, animals, or even God to explore!

Study the PLACE

(HINT HINT... *search for maps online or use a Bible atlas for help.*)

DESCRIBE THE LOCATION (THINK CITIES, NATIONS, ETC.):

_____
_____
_____
_____
_____
_____
_____

DESCRIBE THE CULTURE & PEOPLE OF THE TIME:

_____
_____
_____
_____
_____
_____
_____
_____
_____
_____
_____
_____

Draw the MAP

(A LITTLE TIP. . . if you can't freehand draw it, trace it.)

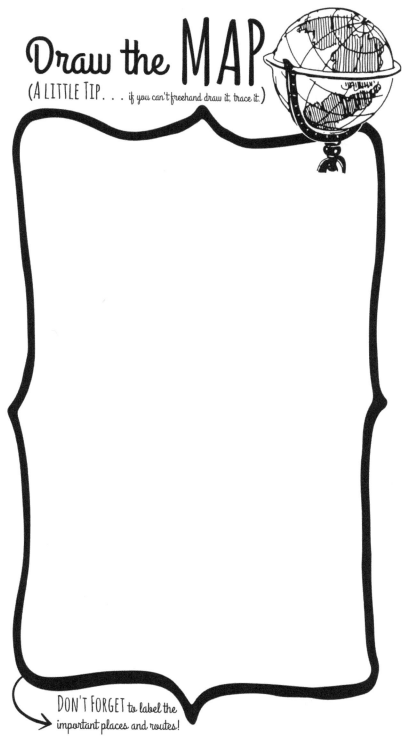

DON'T FORGET to label the important places and routes!

List the BIG THEMES

(HINT HINT. . . such as faith, mercy, love, redemption, justice, etc.)

➡️ THEME(S): _____

_____

➡️ VERSE REFERENCE(S): _____

_____

doodle & write about it

Reflect & think about how it applies to my LIFE . . .

{

_____

_____

_____

_____

_____

_____

_____

_____

_____

_____

_____

Go tell SOMEONE!

WHO can I tell this week?

_____

WHEN & WHERE will it happen?

_____
_____

WHAT do I want to say?

_____
_____
_____

WHY do I want to tell them?

_____
_____
_____

HOW did THE PERSON receive it?

_____
_____
_____

WHO else can I share this BOOK with?

_____

Spread the GOOD NEWS everyday . . .

extra NOTES

extra NOTES

My BOOK choice this week:

DATE:

name:

- - - - - - - - - - - - - - - -

number of chapters: - - - -
(TIP: divide by 6 for a per day reading plan.)

My GOALS for this book study . . . . .

_____

_____

_____

_____

_____

_____

_____

_____

_____

_____

week's READING LOG

☐ date:
   chapter and verses:

☐ date:
   chapter and verses:

☐ date:
   chapter and verses:

☐ date:
   chapter and verses:

☐ date:
   chapter and verses:

☐ date:
   chapter and verses:

☐ date:
   chapter and verses:

☐ date:
   chapter and verses:

☐ date:
   chapter and verses:

☐ date:
   chapter and verses:

☐ date:
   chapter and verses:

☐ date:
   chapter and verses:

TIPS: Read all chapters or only select passages.
Split it up over 6 days with one day of rest.

Choose 3 FAVORITE verses:

1) _____
   _____
   _____

2) _____
   _____
   _____

3) _____
   _____
   _____

Draw & doodle one

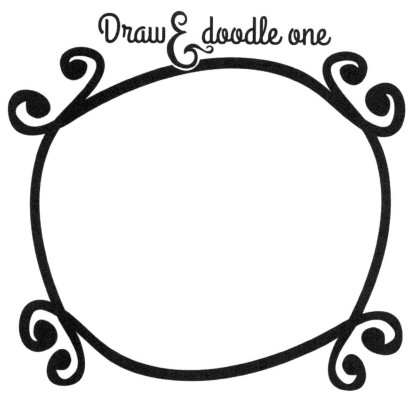

Now RESEARCH it a bit:

1. Who is the AUTHOR?

_____

2. Who was it WRITTEN to or about?

_____

_____

3. What TIME in history did it happen?

_____

_____

4. What PLACE or location is the setting?

_____

_____

5. Who are the main CHARACTERS?

_____

_____

Pick 3 CHARACTERS
& investigate more below:

1) NAME: _____

VERSE REFERENCE(S): _____

SUMMARY: _____

_____

_____

2) NAME: _____

VERSE REFERENCE(S): _____

SUMMARY: _____

_____

_____

3) NAME: _____

VERSE REFERENCE(S): _____

SUMMARY: _____

_____

_____

TIP: Characters don't have to be individual people.
Use nations, tribes, animals, or even God to explore!

Study the PLACE

(HINT HINT. . . . search for maps online or use a Bible atlas for help.)

DESCRIBE THE LOCATION (THINK CITIES, NATIONS, ETC.):

_____

_____

_____

_____

_____

_____

DESCRIBE THE CULTURE & PEOPLE OF THE TIME:

_____

_____

_____

_____

_____

_____

_____

_____

_____

_____

_____

Draw the MAP

(A LITTLE TIP. . . . if you can't freehand draw it, trace it.)

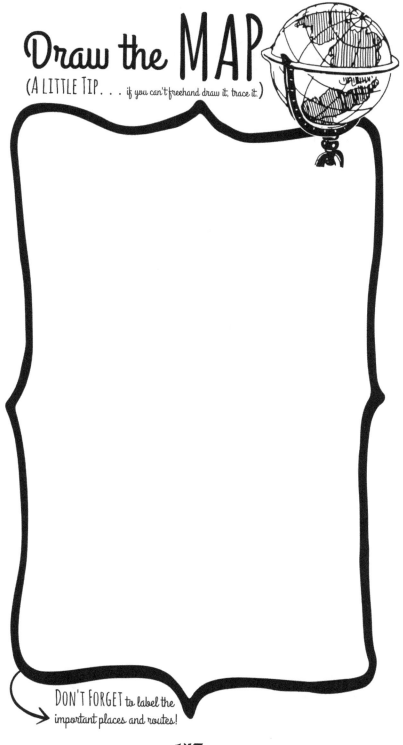

DON'T FORGET to label the important places and routes!

List the BIG THEMES

(HINT HINT. . . such as faith, mercy, love, redemption, justice, etc.)

➡ THEME(S): _____

_____

➡ VERSE REFERENCE(S): _____

_____

_____

doodle & write about it

Reflect & think about how it applies to my LIFE . . .

{

_____

_____

_____

_____

_____

_____

_____

_____

_____

_____

_____

_____

_____

_____

Go tell SOMEONE!

WHO can I tell this week?

_____

WHEN & WHERE will it happen?

_____

WHAT do I want to say?

_____

_____

WHY do I want to tell them?

_____

_____

HOW did THE PERSON receive it?

_____

_____

WHO else can I share this BOOK with?

_____

Spread the GOOD NEWS everyday . . . .

extra NOTES

extra NOTES

extra NOTES

CONGRATULATIONS!

. . . you did it . . .

Don't stop your BOOK-BY-BOOK ➤ Bible study journey now.

Keep on READING it, thinking about it,

ABSORBING its message, &

APPLYING it to YOUR LIFE daily!

1.2.3... journal it!

find more about us at www.123journalit.com
... self-guided DIY study books for the whole family ...

CPSIA information can be obtained
at www.ICGtesting.com
Printed in the USA
BVHW031812171021
619163BV00013B/218